SCOOBY DOO

ANNUAL 2018

D0307094

CONTENTS

SCOOBY DOOBY DOO!

GET TO KNOW
THE GANG:
SCOOBY-DOO & SHAGGY

SCOOBY FUN FILE!

Real name: Scoobert Doo
Nicknames: Scooby-Doo, Scoob
Species: Dog
Role in gang: Eater of all the snacks
Likes: Scooby Snacks, pizza, ice cream
Dislikes: Ghouls, banshees, werewolves
Catchphrase: Scooby Dooby Doo!

ZOINKS!

FUN FACT
Scooby-Doo is a spotted Great Dane.

SCOOBY DOOBY DOO!

SHAGGY FUN FILE!

Real name: Norville Rogers
Nicknames: Shaggy, Raggy, Shag
Species: Human
Role in gang: Best friend to Scooby-Doo
Likes: Scooby Snacks, tofu burgers, fries
Dislikes: Monsters, vampires, creepy clowns
Catchphrase: Zoinks!

PUZZLE FUN
(with Scooby & Shaggy)

Help Scooby-Doo and Shaggy work out these baffling brainteasers!

COLLAR COUNT

How many times does Scooby's dog tag appear above? Write your answer in the box provided.

....

LIKE, WHERE DID YOU GO, DAPHNE?

THE CASE OF THE DISAPPEARING DAMSEL!

Ruh-roh, Daphne Blake has disappeared. She was last seen shopping for clothes at the Crystal Cove Mall. One moment she was standing there, the next she was gone.

Can you solve the mystery? Turn to page 22 for your first clue.

SAME GAME!

Look closely at these words. Can you spot what they all have in common? Write your answer in the space below.

HOUND   **CANINE**

PUP   **MUTT**

POOCH   **BOWWOW**

....

RUN FOR YOUR WIFE!

Whenever monsters appear, Scooby and Shaggy are nowhere near! Look carefully at these sequences, then decide what comes next. Write the colour in the white boxes.

SNACK POT!

Help Scooby and Shaggy reach the Scooby Snacks, making sure to gobble up the other munchies as you go!

START

RECEDING AIRLINES

YOU MEAN A GHOST IS HAUNTING YOUR AIRPLANES?

IT CERTAINLY *LOOKS* THAT WAY. BUT IT'S NOT JUST *ANY* GHOST...

IT'S *HER* GHOST!

CORDELIA FAIRHEART?!

BUT THAT *CAN'T* BE, MISTER SIKORSKY! CORDELIA FAIRHEART'S THE MOST FAMOUS *FEMALE PILOT* IN HISTORY!

OR AT LEAST SHE *WAS*, UNTIL SHE AND HER PLANE *DISAPPEARED* OVER THE OCEAN EIGHTY YEARS AGO!

LOOK, I DON'T KNOW WHETHER THIS GHOST IS *REAL* OR NOT. EITHER WAY, SHE KEEPS *APPEARING* DURING OUR FLIGHTS--AND IT'S STARTING TO *SCARE OFF* OUR CUSTOMERS!

THAT'S WHY I NEED YOUR HELP.

WE'LL BE GLAD TO DO WHAT WE CAN.

AS LONG AS WE CAN DO IT RIGHT HERE ON THE *GROUND*! LIKE, FLYING SCARES ME ALMOST AS MUCH--

DCCO26227

JUST PLANE SPOOKED

WRITER: SHOLLY FISCH
PENCILS: ROBERT POPE
INKS: SCOTT MCRAE
COLOR: HEROIC AGE   LETTERS: DEZI SIENTY
ASSISTANT EDITOR: SARAH LITT
EDITOR: KWANZA JOHNSON

IF WE SUDDENLY LOSE AIR PRESSURE, *OXYGEN MASKS* WILL DROP FROM THE CEILING.

L-LOSE *AIR* PRESSURE...? O-*OXYGEN MASKS*...?

IN THE EVENT OF A WATER LANDING, THERE IS A *LIFE VEST* UNDER YOUR SEAT. TO *INFLATE* THE VEST, PULL THESE TABS...

"L-LIFE VEST?" W-WE NEED *L-LIFE VESTS?!*

LIKE, LEMME OUTTA THIS *DEATH TRAP!*

DID HE SAY...*DEATH TRAP?*

≷GULP!≷ LIKE, W-WHERE'S THE *GROUND?*

WE *TOOK OFF* ALREADY. UM, BY THE WAY, I DON'T THINK *REAL* FLIGHT ATTENDANTS *PANIC* LIKE THAT WHILE THEY EXPLAIN SAFETY PROCEDURES.

WE'RE SUPPOSED TO BE *UNDERCOVER*, REMEMBER?

RETZEL?

I, UH, HOPE YOU ENJOYED OUR LITTLE, UH, *COMEDY SKIT.* THERE WILL BE MORE, UH, *IN-FLIGHT ENTERTAINMENT* LATER.

JINKIES! HERE COMES LINDY!

HIDE, SCOOB! IF ANYONE SEES YOU, YOU'LL SPEND THE REST OF THE FLIGHT IN A *PET CARRIER!*

RUH-HUH!

PRETZELS

OOOH, PRETZELS.

WHAT'S THE BIG IDEA OF THAT *STUNT* YOU PULLED OUT THERE?! YOU COULD HAVE STARTED A *PANIC!* IF I HADN'T--

AAAIIIEEEEEEE!

NOW WHAT?

TURN BACK! OR THIS FLIGHT IS *DOOMED!*

CORDELIA FAIRHEART!

...RELLO? ...RAGGY?

W-WHAT'S GOING ON?

WHAT DID SHE MEAN, D-DOOMED?

LET US OFF!

EVERYONE! THERE'S NO DANGER! THAT WAS JUST OUR...UH, 3-D MOVIE!

PLEASE RETURN TO YOUR SEATS!

OKAY, AT LEAST EVERYONE'S STARTING TO CALM DOWN. BUT WHERE'S CORDELIA?

I DON'T KNOW. SHE DISAPPEARED WHILE WE WERE BUSY SETTLING DOWN THE PASSENGERS.

AND WHERE'S SHAGGY?

I DON'T SEE HIM ANYWH--

Z-Z-ZOIIIIINNKS!

LIKE, I GUESS IT'S TRUE...

THINGS IN THE OVERHEAD COMPARTMENTS DO SHIFT DURING THE FLIGHT...

WHAT'S GOING ON? IT SOUNDS LIKE A *RIOT* OUT HERE!

UH... SHOULDN'T YOU BE, LIKE, *FLYING THE PLANE?*

I'M THE *CO-PILOT!* NOW, WHAT'S THE EMERGENCY? DO WE NEED TO *TURN AROUND?*

I'M SURE THAT WON'T BE NECESSARY. IT WAS ANOTHER CORDELIA FAIRHEART SIGHTING, BUT IT'S *OVER* NOW.

CAPTAIN ORVILLE AND I WILL MAKE THAT DECISION -- *AFTER I* CHECK *EVERY INCH* OF THIS PLANE!

DO YOU THINK SHE'LL FIND CORDELIA?

I JUST HOPE SHE DOESN'T FIND *SCOOBY!*

IT'S *STRANGE,* THOUGH...

WHAT?

CHECK THE *SIGN!* THE PASSENGERS HAVE HAD THEIR SEAT BELTS *FASTENED* EVER SINCE WE TOOK OFF.

IF EVERYONE WAS IN THEIR *SEATS,* HOW COULD SOMEONE PRETEND TO BE CORDELIA?

UNLESS...SHE REALLY *IS* A GHOST!

RAGGY? ROO-HOO!

RIKES! A RHOST!

A DOG?

R-RELLLLLLP!

HEY! COME *BACK* HERE!

I-I MEAN--

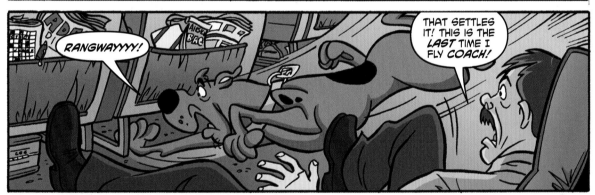

NO PROBLEM, BUDDY! *I'LL* GET YOU LOOSE!

SHAGGY

POP

OOPS.

HUH?

≈OOOFF!≈

LIKE, THAT'S WHAT I CALL AN *UNHAPPY* LANDING!

HEY! THE LIFE VEST KNOCKED OFF CORDELIA'S *MASK!*

AND *UNDERNEATH* IT IS--

--THE PLANE'S CO-PILOT, *NELLY ARMSTRONG!*

RECEDING AIRLINES

LATER--

I CAN'T *BELIEVE* IT! ONE OF OUR OWN CO-PILOTS, PRETENDING TO BE A *GHOST?*

APPARENTLY, ANOTHER AIRLINE WANTED TO HIRE HER AND CAPTAIN *ORVILLE* FOR *MORE MONEY,* BUT THEY WERE UNDER CONTRACT TO WORK FOR *YOU.*

THEY FIGURED THE ONLY WAY OUT WAS TO *SCARE OFF* YOUR CUSTOMERS AND DRIVE YOUR AIRLINE *OUT OF BUSINESS.*

UNBELIEVABLE! IT WOULD HAVE BEEN SO MUCH SIMPLER IF THEY JUST CAME AND *TALKED* TO ME.

WELL, I OWE YOU KIDS MY *THANKS,* AND YOU'VE CERTAINLY EARNED A *REWARD.*

NO, WE COULDN'T POSSIBLY...

WELL, MAYBE WE *COULD!* LIKE, WHAT'S THE REWARD? SOME OF THOSE FROZEN *IN-FLIGHT MEALS?*

"F-F-FLY?"

COULDN'T WE JUST HAVE SOME MORE *PRETZELS* INSTEAD?

EVEN BETTER! *FREE AIRLINE TICKETS* TO FLY ANYWHERE YOU WANT!

THE END

THE MYSTERY MACHINE EXPLORED!

Vans don't come much cooler than The Mystery Machine. Let's take a look around the gang's awesome wheels...

THIS HOUND SURE KNOWS HOW TO GET AROUND!

✳ Roof rack (for carrying large equipment)

✳ Removable roof (perfect for springing traps)

✳ Driver's cab (amazingly, this fits the entire gang)

✳ Cool design (this was done by the van's original owner, Flash Flannigan, a keyboard player in a band called the Mystery Kids)

✳ Roomy rear (perfect for carrying lots of mystery-solving equipment such as computers, ladders, torches and ropes)

✳ Funky hub caps!

✳ Spare tyre (in case of emergency)

SURVEILLANCE FOOTAGE!

The mall's security cameras show four ghoulish figures stalking Daphne as she shops. The footage also shows Daphne being grabbed, but not who grabbed her. Darn it! But at least now we know why she disappeared. She was kidnapped.

Turn to page 28 to meet the first of our possible kidnappers...

The back of The Mystery Machine is the perfect place for enjoying a snack... or 10.

KNOCK KNOCK, ROO'S THERE?

Let your friends and family know what kind of day you're having with this fun door hanger!

YOU WILL NEED
• Scissors
• Glue

BE SMART AND ASK AN ADULT FOR HELP WITH THIS TASK.

INSTRUCTIONS:

1. Glue this page to a piece of thin card.

2. Wait until the glue is dry then cut out the hanger along the dotted lines.

3. Fold the template in half along the centre line.

4. Glue the two sides together.

5. Hang the hanger from your door handle!

SCOOBY-DOO, WHERE ARE YOU?

CREEPY CRYPT
**Scooby-Doo and Shaggy are hiding from the Mummy of Ankha.
Look carefully at this scene – can you spot the cowardly custards?**

CIRCUS OF FEAR
**Can you spot Scooby-Doo and Shaggy in this
scene before the Ghost Clown does? Be quick!**

24

GET TO KNOW THE GANG: DAPHNE

DAPHNE FUN FILE!

Real name: Daphne Blake
Nicknames: Danger-prone Daphne, Miss Blake
Species: Human
Role in gang: Where Daphne goes, trouble follows!
Likes: Singing, karate, clothes
Dislikes: Gargoyles, witches, headless horsemen
Catchphrase: Jeepers!

JEEPERS!

FUN FACT
Daphne has a black belt in karate.

SECRET FACT
Daphne's family has a butler named Jenkins.

LOST AND FOUND
Daphne has dropped her green scarf. Can you guide her through the maze to reach it, making sure to avoid the monsters?

START

PUZZLE FUN
(with Daphne)

Team up with Daphne to get to the bottom of these mind-twisters!

Find the four pairs of matching Daphnes. It's not as easy as it looks!

DUPLICATING DAPHNE!

LOOKING GOOD!

If there's one thing Daphne loves more than solving mysteries, it's clothes! Create a groovy new design for Miss Blake's dress and then colour it in.

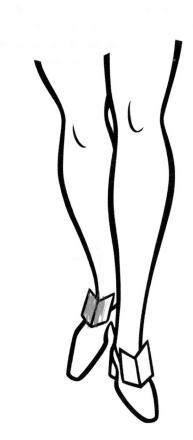

WORD FUN!

How many words can you make using the letters in **DAPHNE BLAKE**? We've done one to start you off.

HAND

. . . .

. . . .

. . . .

. . . .

. . . .

. . . .

SCOOBY DOO
AND THE TANK OF TERRORS

A spooky Scooby mystery!

Ruh-roh! A ghost diver is haunting the local aquarium. Now it's up to Scooby and his friends to unmask that spooky snorkeler!

SUSPECT #1
SWAMP ZOMBIE
This lumbering lunatic is smarter than he looks. From scaring to spelling, he's the top monster in town, and kidnapping a member of Mystery, Inc would confirm that!

Turn to page 34 to meet our second suspect.

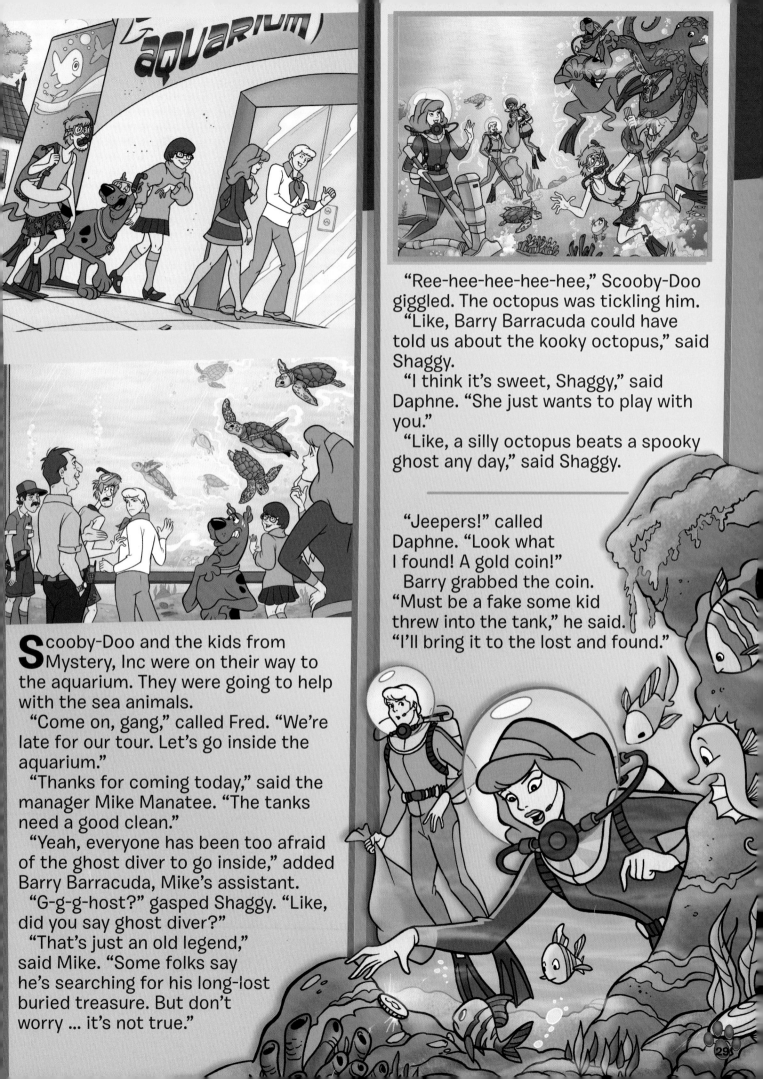

"Ree-hee-hee-hee-hee," Scooby-Doo giggled. The octopus was tickling him.

"Like, Barry Barracuda could have told us about the kooky octopus," said Shaggy.

"I think it's sweet, Shaggy," said Daphne. "She just wants to play with you."

"Like, a silly octopus beats a spooky ghost any day," said Shaggy.

"Jeepers!" called Daphne. "Look what I found! A gold coin!"

Barry grabbed the coin. "Must be a fake some kid threw into the tank," he said. "I'll bring it to the lost and found."

Scooby-Doo and the kids from Mystery, Inc were on their way to the aquarium. They were going to help with the sea animals.

"Come on, gang," called Fred. "We're late for our tour. Let's go inside the aquarium."

"Thanks for coming today," said the manager Mike Manatee. "The tanks need a good clean."

"Yeah, everyone has been too afraid of the ghost diver to go inside," added Barry Barracuda, Mike's assistant.

"G-g-g-host?" gasped Shaggy. "Like, did you say ghost diver?"

"That's just an old legend," said Mike. "Some folks say he's searching for his long-lost buried treasure. But don't worry ... it's not true."

That's when the gang got another surprise.

"Zoinks! The ghost diver," cried Shaggy. "Like, let's make some waves!"

Scooby and the gang swam across the tank as fast as they could.

Fred spied a cave. The gang slipped inside and waited until the diver disappeared again.

"Jeepers," said Daphne. "That was close. But why is there a cave in the aquarium?"

"It's a storage closet," said Fred. "Look! There's a vacuum in here."

"That isn't a vacuum," said Velma. "It's a metal detector."

Before the gang could find out more, something found them.

"Ree-hee-hee-hee-hee," Scooby-Doo giggled. Only it wasn't the octopus tickling him, it was the ghost diver!

"Like, that spooky snorkeler is back!" cried Shaggy.

The gang was on the run again. With the ghost diver closing in, they needed a hiding place – fast.

"Look!" cried Daphne. "Let's go into the old mini-sub ride!"

"Jinkies," said Velma. "Look at these maps of the tanks. Someone has been busy searching for something."

"I bet I know who," added Fred.

"I know what the ghost diver is looking for," said Daphne, holding up another gold coin.

"Wait a minute," said Velma. "I've seen that coin before. A few years ago, someone stole a hundred coins like that from the aquarium's buried treasure display. No one has ever found the coins or the thief."

Daphne nodded. "The thief must have hidden the coins in another part of the aquarium – like the tank."

"Okay, gang," said Fred. "It's time to set a trap and catch this creepy ghost crook. I know just how to do it."

"Like, please don't say me and Scoob are the bait," said Shaggy.

But Fred's plan was already in place. He'd set up a big net in one of the tanks. As usual, Scooby and Shaggy were the bait.

"Roh rell," sighed Scooby.

"Like, it would be nice if we could choose our part in the plan just once," moaned Shaggy.

Fred, Daphne and Velma waited for the ghost diver to come after Scooby and Shaggy. Then they turned on the tank's whirlpool. The water jets pushed the net right into the ghost diver. Soon he was all tangled up.

The gang pulled the ghost diver out of the tank. "I think it's about time we find out who's hiding under this helmet," said Fred.

"Barry Barracuda!" cried Mike Manatee. "You're the one who stole the coins!"

"We should have known it was you when you grabbed the coin away from Daphne," said Velma.

"I'd be rich if it weren't for you meddling kids," cried Barry.

"Scooby-Dooby-Doo," howled Scooby. He and the gang had saved the day once more.

THE END

EAT AN ENERGY BOOSTING SCOOBY SNACK. Take another turn.

SCOOBY SNACKS

THE SPOOKY SPACE KOOK ATTACKS! Miss a go!

ZOINKS! A FLAT TYRE! Miss a go while you wait for help!

HOLD UP GANG, DEAD END! Reverse 4 spaces and try again.

FINISH!

THE PHANTOM SHADOW LEAPS OUT AT YOU! Reverse 2 spaces.

THE MYSTERY MACHINE SKIDS ON SOME GOO! Slide forward 1 space.

33

IT'S TIME TO GUESS THE CRIME!

Thanks to Mystery, Inc, another villain has been unmasked. But what crime would he have gotten away with if it hadn't been for those meddling kids? To find out, solve the clues in this poem. There is a secret letter to discover in each verse. We've done the first one for you.

My first is in **SPOOK**
And also in **VIRUS**

My second is in **MASK**
But not in **CASKET**

My third is in **MONSTROUS**
But not in **MONSTER**

My fourth is in **GHOUL**
And also in **GIANT**

My fifth is in **GHOST**
But not in **HOST**

My sixth is in **CLOWN**
And also in **LIZARD**

My seventh is in **WITCH**
But not in **WATCH OUT**

My eighth is in **NIGHT**
But not in **FRIGHT**

My ninth is in **GHASTLY**
And also in **GRIM**

WRITE THE CRIME HERE!

S.... ....

SUSPECT #2
Miner Forty-Niner
This dastardly digger's greed knows no bounds. He'd love to get his hands on the Blake family fortune.

Find out more about our third suspect on page 37

34

GET TO KNOW THE GANG: FRED

LET'S SPLIT UP, GANG!

SECRET FACT
Fred is allergic to cats.

FUN FACT
Fred loves building traps.

THE NAME GAME

Can you think of nine words to describe FRED JONES starting with each of the letters in his name? We've done the first one for you!

Fearless
R
E
D

J
O
N
E
S

FRED FUN FILE!

Real name: Fredrick Herman Jones
Nicknames: Fred, Freddy
Species: Human
Role in gang: Driver of The Mystery Machine
Likes: Inventing things, splitting up, saving the day
Dislikes: Rampaging robots, mummies, spectres
Catchphrase: Let's split up, gang!

PUZZLE FUN
(with Freddy)

Hold the phone, Fred's in trouble! Help our handy hero out by solving these puzzlers.

MACHINE MUDDLE

Yikes! The Mystery Machine's in a bit of a mess after a run in with **this guy!** Help Fred rebuild it by writing the correct order into the spaces opposite.

MEMORY TEST!

Look closely at these words describing Fred, then cover them up and see how many you can remember.

HERO HANDSOME
DRIVER BRAVE
TRAP LEADER
SLEUTH

Using the grid above as a guide, copy the picture of Freddy into the empty boxes opposite. Then colour it in!

FRED RINGER!

Can you spot the two identical pictures of Fred Jones?

SUSPECT #3
Sea Demon
This gilled ghoul has a long-standing feud with Nedley and Elizabeth Blake. Did he snatch their daughter Daphne out of spite?

Our fourth and final suspect is revealed on page 48.

GANG, MY HIGH SCHOOL FRIEND, **MEIKO**, IS IN TROUBLE!

DOES HER LETTER GIVE ANY **CLUES**, DAPHNE?

ONLY THAT **STRANGE THINGS** ARE HAPPENING AT HER AUNT'S RESTAURANT, THE FAMOUS **YUMMAGUCHI**, AND THE CUSTOMERS ARE GETTING **SCARED OFF**.

IF THIS KEEPS UP, HER AUNT'S RESTAURANT WILL BE FORCED TO CLOSE!

SOUNDS **FISHY**. GET IT, SCOOB?! JAPANESE RESTAURANT... **FISHY!**

REE-HEE-HEE-HEE! **RISHY!**

HERE'S THE YUMMAGUCHI. LOOKS **SPOOKY-OOKY**, FREDDY.

YEAH, IF IT'S SPOOKY **OUTSIDE**, WHO KNOWS WHAT IT'S LIKE **INSIDE!?**

G-G-G-G HOSTS!

ZOINKS! A STAMPEDE!

HAUNTED SAMURAIS!

GET OUTTA THE WAY!

HEY, YOU KIDS. I WOULDN'T GO IN THERE IF I WERE YOU.

THEY SAY THE PLACE IS **HAUNTED.**

RAUNTED?!?

YEAH. SO IF YOU WANT A GOOD MEAL WITH **NO GHOSTS**, COME OVER TO **MY** PLACE NEXT DOOR.

"HARRY'S HAMBURGERS." I HAVE THE HOTTEST GRILL THIS SIDE OF PEORIA.

THANKS, BUT WE HAVE BUSINESS **INSIDE**.

WELL, DON'T SAY I DIDN'T **WARN** YA!

WRITER - JYMN MAGON
PENCILLER - SCOTT JERALDS
INKER - JACK PURCELL

COLORIST - HEROIC AGE
LETTERER - JOHN J. HILL
EDITOR - MICHAEL SIGLAIN

SUSHI ME? SUSHI YOU!

I WONDER WHAT'S SCARING THE CUSTOMERS OFF.

MEIKO SAID THAT *EERIE THINGS* KEEP HAPPENING.

WHAT COULD BE *EERIE* IN A *FAMILY* RESTAURANT??

KIND OF *SLOW* AROUND HERE, HUH?

ANY SLOWER AND A *TURTLE* WILL GET MY JOB.

DO YOU HAVE ANY IDEA WHAT COULD BE CAUSING ALL THESE *STRANGE EVENTS*?

WELL, MEIKO NOTICED THAT WEIRD STUFF STARTED HAPPENING *RIGHT AFTER* HER AUNT HUNG THOSE NEW DECORATIONS.

THEY LOOK LIKE 14TH CENTURY *SAMURAI* ARTIFACTS.

YES, THEY CAME FROM THE *TEMPLE* OF SOME *DEAD WARLORD.* I THINK THEY MIGHT BE... *CURSED.*

AND NOW I'LL LIGHT THE *"VOLCANO."* DON'T WORRY, IT'LL ONLY BE A SMALL ERUPTION.

CURSED? IN WHAT WAY?

GAH!!!

WHOA!!!

WHOOSH

NEVER MIND. I THINK I GET THE *POINT!*

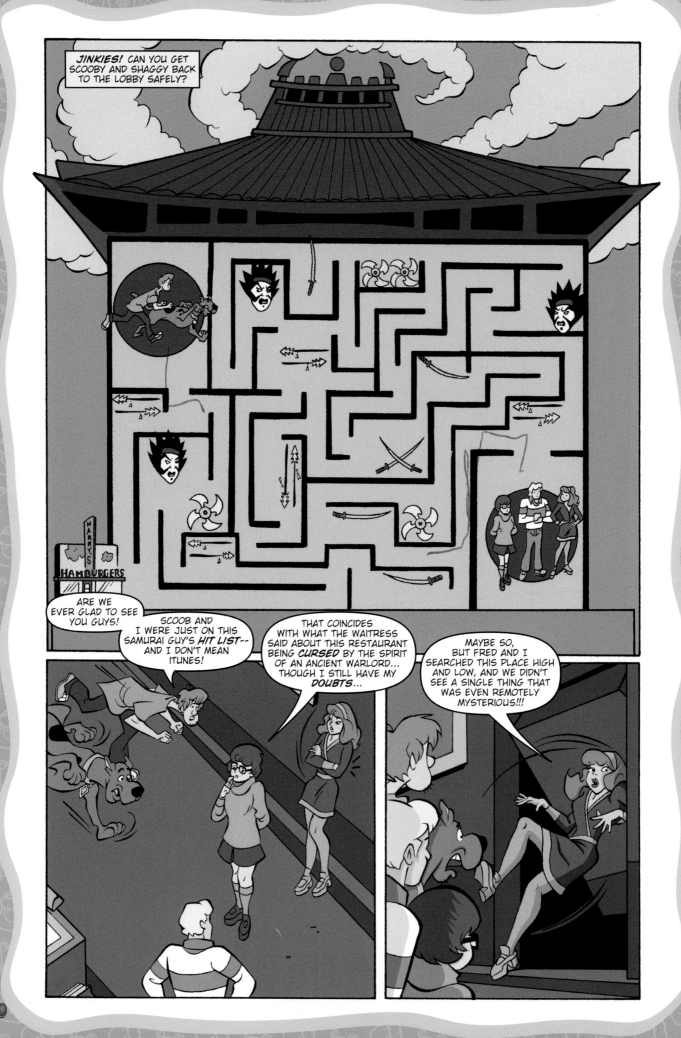

MEIKO, IT'S *YOU!*

HURRY, UNTIE ME, DAPHNE. HE'S COMING BACK.

WHO'S COMING BACK?

AEE!!!!

HIM!

IT'S *HAMBURGER HARRY!*

YES-- THE *OWNER* OF THE *RESTAURANT* NEXT DOOR.

TODAY WHEN I DISCOVERED THAT *HE* WAS CREATING ALL THIS SCARY STUFF, HE *KIDNAPPED* ME.

HE WANTED TO SHUT DOWN THE *YUMMAGUCHI* SO THAT *HIS* BUSINESS WOULD PICK UP.

AND I WOULD HAVE GOTTEN AWAY WITH IT, TOO, IF IT HADN'T BEEN FOR THIS *PESKY WAITRESS!*

THAT SOUNDS FAMILIAR-- BUT *DIFFERENT.*

WHEN HARRY SAID HE HAD THE *HOTTEST GRILL* AROUND, I FIGURED THERE MIGHT BE A CONNECTION WITH THAT HUGE "VOLCANO" FLAME.

LIKE, THANKS FOR LETTING *US* KNOW, VELMA!

THANKS FOR FINDING ME, DAPHNE! AND THANKS FOR SAVING MY AUNT'S RESTAURANT, GUYS!

WELL, LIKE, *SAYONARA.* SCOOBY AND I ARE OFF TO THE KITCHEN FOR SOME RAW FISH. I GUESS YOU'LL *SASHIMI* LATER!

REAH! RAYONARA!

THE END!

CRACK THE CODE!

Velma has been sent a mysterious message on her handheld. But what does it say? Use the key below to find out!

ZMW R
DLFOW SZEV
TLGGVM
ZDZB DRGS
RG GLL, RU
RG DVIVM'G
ULI BLF
NVWWORMT
PRWH!

ARE YOU THINKING WHAT I'M THINKING?

KEY

A	B	C	D	E	F	G	H	I	J	K	L	M
Z	Y	X	W	V	U	T	S	R	Q	P	O	N

N	O	P	Q	R	S	T	U	V	W	X	Y	Z
M	L	K	J	I	H	G	F	E	D	C	B	A

WRITE THE MESSAGE HERE!

....
....
....
....
....
....

44

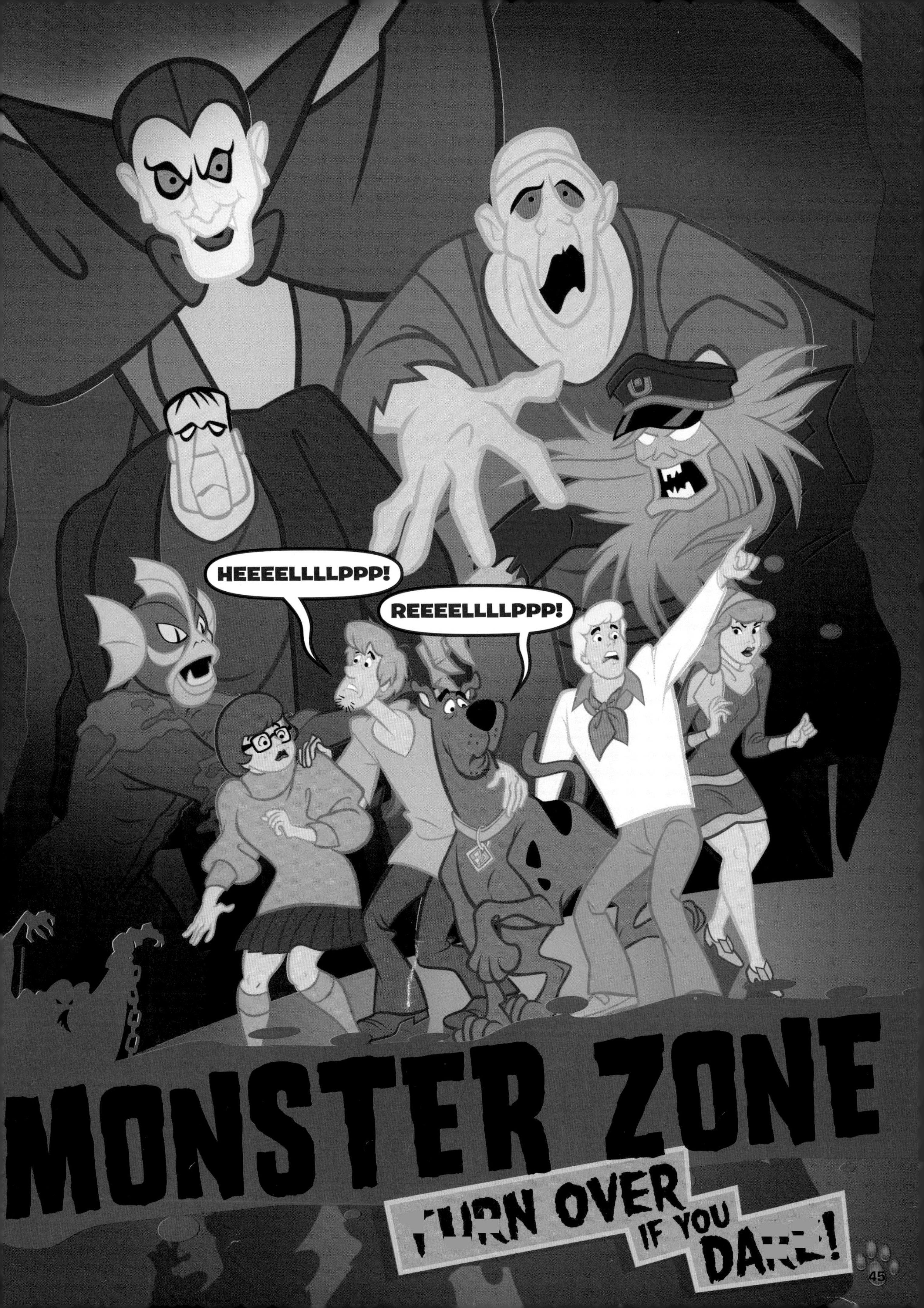
HEEEELLLLPPP!
REEEELLLLPPP!
MONSTER ZONE
RN OVER
IF YOU
DA !

Watch out – bad guys about! Complete the names of these Scooby villains, using the big letters at the bottom of this page. Each letter should only be used once!

YOU WILL DO AS YOU ARE TOLD!

* Evil grin
* Horrible laugh
* Hypnotic powers

JINKIES, IT'S THE **GHOST CLO_N**

CREEPER! CREEEEPER!

* Green skin
* Menacing yellow eyes
* Bad temper

JEEPERS, IT'S THE **CREE_ER**

K P W T X

MONSTER ZONE

LIKE, THIS IS SNOW JOKE!

FREAKY FACT
The Snow Ghost was actually Mr. Greenway in disguise.

SPOT THE SPOOKY DIFFERENCES!

There are 10 differences between these two pictures. Can you find them all?

LIKE, THIS IS SNOW JOKE!

SUSPECT #4
Indian Witch Doctor
This manic medic has a history of kidnapping for personal gain. Could heiress Daphne Blake be his latest victim?

Turn to page 55 for your next clue.

48

WRITE A CREEPY STORY!

MYSTERY SOLVERS MONTHLY

Scooby and Shaggy have made the front page of Mystery Solvers Monthly. Write a scary story to match this picture!

WRITING TIP!
Think about when and where your story takes place and what characters are involved. Then add lots and lots of spooky details!

MONSTER ZONE

EERIE FACT
Vampires can only enter your home if they are invited.

SPOOKY SUDOKU!

Can you complete these petrifying picture puzzles? Each row, column and 4x4 mini grid must have one of each monster.

50

MONSTROUS WORD SEARCH!

JEEPERS, THAT'S A LOT OF MONSTERS!

See if you can find these creepy creatures. Words can go up, down, diagonally and backwards.

SCARY FACT
Witches often have pets such as cats, owls or toads. They are known as 'familiars'.

SKELETON
GHOST
PHANTOM
VAMPIRE

DEMON
GARGOYLE
CREEPER
WEREWOLF

GHOUL
APEMAN
MUTANT
BEAST

X	W	I	K	C	H	F	D	N	I	F	C	H	R
M	L	U	A	M	Z	W	F	D	P	D	R	V	V
G	A	R	G	O	Y	L	E	A	K	S	E	B	A
H	R	F	A	V	I	S	S	Y	D	F	E	D	M
O	E	J	G	U	Q	F	S	A	P	K	P	N	P
S	K	E	L	E	T	O	N	Y	L	P	E	V	I
T	L	Q	U	S	N	F	X	K	A	O	R	Z	R
N	A	Z	C	W	E	R	E	W	O	L	F	F	E
A	M	L	H	B	C	X	S	W	H	T	R	Z	H
M	A	H	G	T	N	C	G	B	U	W	K	A	M
E	K	U	S	C	Z	H	M	O	T	N	A	H	P
P	S	A	W	A	O	F	C	B	H	I	F	U	D
A	E	M	V	U	Z	N	O	M	E	D	U	L	P
B	A	K	L	S	L	M	X	T	N	A	T	U	M

51

MONSTER ZONE

What does the Titanic Twist serve for dessert? Ice Scream.

Why did the Mummy of Ankha have no friends? He was too wrapped up in himself.

Why didn't the Swamp Zombie get the job? They wanted somebody more lively.

Why was Charlie the Robot angry? Because someone kept pushing his buttons.

REE-HEE-HEE!

GHOULISH GIGGLES!

Make your friends and family scream with laughter with these jumpy jokes!

Where does Dracula keep his money? In a blood bank.

What is the Ghost of Redbeard's favourite film? Booty and the Beast.

Where does Cornfield Clem go on holiday? The Isle of Fright!

SHOE CLUE

Daphne's high heel has been found in the mall car park, with four different fingerprints on it. One of these prints belongs to Daphne, but can you identify the other three?

52

GET TO KNOW THE GANG: VELMA

VELMA FUN FILE!

Real name: Velma Dinkley
Nicknames: Velm, V
Species: Human
Role in gang: The brains of the bunch
Likes: Deciphering clues, solving mysteries, science stuff, finding her glasses
Dislikes: Zombies, phantoms, apemen
Catchphrase: Jinkies!

JINKIES!

SECRET FACT

Velma has her own wrestling move – the Flying Dinkley!

SPOOK SPOT!

Are you a hotshot investigator just like Velma? Let's find out! There are 10 mini ghosts hidden on these two pages – can you spot them all?

FUN FACT

Velma is a genius.

53

PUZZLE FUN

(with Velma)

Velma's the brains of the gang but even she needs a helping hand now and then. Save the day together by cracking these conundrums...

EYE TEST!

- Jinkies, Velma has dropped her glasses and we all know she can't see without her glasses. Can you work out who or what V is looking at?

MISSING OBJECT

Velma never goes anywhere without her mystery-solving kit. Look closely at these two pictures – can you spot the item that's disappeared?

MONSTER UNMASKED!

Which villain has Velma snared? Join the dots to find out, then colour him in!

True Or False
Velma Dinkley is the youngest member of Mystery, Inc.

....

EYEWITNESS ACCOUNT
On the day of the kidnapping, the mall's parking attendant saw a woman fitting Daphne's description being bundled into a car. He tried to help, but the vehicle sped off. Although the attendant didn't see the driver, he distinctly heard the woman shout: "Let me go, you green meanie!"

Your final clue can be found on page 67.

55

IS SOMEONE THERE?

I SAID, "IS ANYONE..."

≈Gasp!≈

WB# DCC022537

THE MISSING MUMMY MYSTERY

WRITER: *JOHN ROZUM*   ARTIST: *SCOTT NEELY*   COLORIST: *HEROIC AGE*
LETTERER: *TRAVIS LANHAM*   EDITOR: *HARVEY RICHARDS*

THEN WHAT HAPPENED, SIR WEMPLE?

AFTER THE POLICE ARRIVED I SENT MR. MANNERS--THE NIGHT GUARD--HOME. I TOLD HIM TO TAKE A VACATION, BUT HE REFUSED. HE SAID HE WOULDN'T HEAR OF IT.

BUT *WHY*? IT SURE SOUNDS LIKE HE COULD USE ONE. POOR MAN.

LIKE, *NOT US.* I COUNT *FIVE* UNOPENED SARCOPHOGUSUMUSSES WHICH MEANS THE MUMMY HAS FIVE FRIENDS WHO MIGHT DECIDE THEY NEED SOME EXERCISE, TOO.

I'D MUCH RATHER BE *OUTSIDE* THE MUSEUM THAN *IN.*

RHEE TROO.

WELL, THE WAY I LOOK AT IT IS THAT IF THE *LIVING MUMMY* IS SOMEWHERE *OUTSIDE* OF THE MUSEUM, THEN I'D RATHER BE *HERE INSIDE,* WHERE THE MUMMY *ISN'T.*

GREAT IDEA!

RHIT IS?

YOU TWO GO OUTSIDE AND SEE IF ANYONE HAS SEEN ANYTHING. ASK AROUND.

A WALKING MUMMY IS SURE TO HAVE ATTRACTED SOMEONE'S ATTENTION, OR AT LEAST HAVE LEFT SOME CLUES BEHIND.

WHILE YOU TWO ARE DOING THAT, WE'LL SEE WHAT WE CAN FIND OUT HERE.

PLEASE. WE'RE KEEPING THE MUSEUM CLOSED TODAY, BUT I'D LIKE TO REOPEN AS SOON AS POSSIBLE.

MR. MANNERS, WOULD YOU MIND WALKING US THROUGH YOUR EVENING, LEADING UP TO YOUR SIGHTING OF THE WALKING MUMMY?

WELL, LET'S SEE. I ARRIVED AT 11:45 LAST NIGHT, LIKE I ALWAYS DO, TO START THE NIGHT SHIFT.

"AFTER I CHANGED INTO MY UNIFORM, I WENT TO THE GUARD STATION TO RELIEVE STEVE BANNING--HE'S THE GUARD WHO WORKS THE SHIFT BEFORE MINE."

HOW'S IT BEEN, STEVE?

QUIET AS A TOMB, DAVID. JUST LIKE ALWAYS.

"I TOOK MY PLACE BEHIND THE DESK, AND CHECKED THE MONITORS. THE ONLY MOVEMENT ON ANY OF THEM WAS STEVE WALKING TO THE LOCKER ROOM. AFTER A FEW MINUTES, I GOT UP AND BEGAN MY ROUNDS."

IT USUALLY TAKES ABOUT FORTY MINUTES TO COMPLETE MY ROUNDS. NOTHING WAS OUT OF THE ORDINARY UNTIL I ENTERED THE EGYPTIAN WING ABOUT HALF AN HOUR INTO MY ROUNDS. I NEVER FINISHED THEM.

CAN YOU PLAY BACK A RECORDING OF THE TIME THAT YOU REACHED THE EGYPTIAN WING?

NO. THIS IS AN OLD SECURITY SYSTEM. WE ONLY RECORD IF WE SEE ANYTHING UNUSUAL WHILE WE ARE IN THIS ROOM.

WHAT WERE YOU DOING IN THE MUSEUM SO LATE?

I OFTEN WORK LATE AT NIGHT. WHEN THE MUSEUM IS FULLY STAFFED DURING THE DAY, I'M OFTEN INTERRUPTED BY PHONE CALLS AND QUESTIONS FROM OTHER STAFF MEMBERS THAT THE SCHOLARLY ASPECT OF MY WORK HERE FALLS BY THE WAYSIDE.

DID YOU SEE THE WALKING MUMMY?

NO, SIR. I DID NOT. I WAS ALERTED BY THE SOUND OF MR. MANNERS'S CRIES. I WENT TO INVESTIGATE. MY FIRST IMPRESSION IS THAT HE'D BEEN INJURED.

I WONDER HOW SHAGGY AND SCOOBY ARE DOING?

EXCUSE ME, BUT HAVE EITHER OF YOU SEEN A MUMMY?

...ABOUT THAT TALL.

EXCUSE ME, I'M LOOKING FOR A MUMMY...

YOUNG MAN, CAN WE HELP YOU?

WE'RE LOOKING FOR A MUMMY.

AHHH! WHERE DID YOU LAST SEE YOUR MOMMY?

RIGHT HERE IN THE MUSEUM.

AND YOUR MOMMY'S NOT THERE NOW?

NO, THE GUARD SAID IT WALKED OUT THE DOOR.

PROBABLY LOOKING FOR YOU. DON'T WORRY, WE'LL HELP YOU FIND YOUR MOMMY.

OFFICER! THIS YOUNG MAN HERE LOST HIS MOMMY.

I'LL TAKE THEM DOWN TO THE PRECINCT HOUSE AND SEE IF I CAN'T FIND OUT WHERE THEY LIVE.

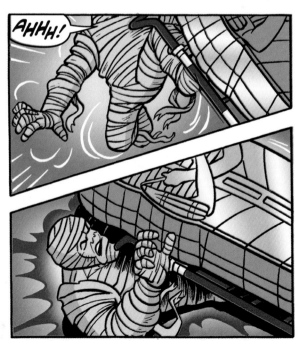

EXCUSE ME, BUT THESE TWO ARE LOOKING FOR THEIR MOMMY.

RIGHT HERE, OFFICER. ONLY I THINK THIS MUMMY WILL BE ACCOMPANYING YOU BACK TO THE POLICE STATION.

STEVE BANNING!

JUST AS I EXPECTED.

WHEN MR. MANNERS AND I FIRST VISITED THE LOCKER ROOM, I NOTICED A STRIP OF *GAUZE BANDAGE* STICKING OUT OF ONE OF THE LOCKERS, AS WELL AS A *DOLLY* FOR MOVING BOXES WHICH HAD NO BUSINESS BEING THERE.

THEN I STARTED PIECING EVENTS TOGETHER.

BANNING HAD HIS CRIME PLANNED WELL. BEING A GUARD, HE HAD ACCESS TO *EVERYTHING*. HE ALSO KNEW THE ROUTINES OF THE GUARDS. WHEN MR. MANNERS RELIEVED HIM OF DUTY, HE NEVER WENT HOME.

HE KNEW THAT MANNERS WOULD BEGIN HIS *ROUNDS* WHILE HE WAS IN THE *LOCKER ROOM*, GIVING HIM PLENTY OF TIME TO CHANGE INTO THE *MUMMY COSTUME* AND TO STATION HIMSELF IN THE EGYPTIAN WING WHERE HE PRETENDED TO COME TO LIFE AND LEAVE.

HE *STOLE* AND HID THE *REAL MUMMY* DURING HIS OWN SHIFT, I'M GUESSING TO SELL TO A PRIVATE COLLECTOR. HE THOUGHT HE'D BE MORE LIKELY TO GET AWAY WITH IT IF PEOPLE THOUGHT THE MUMMY LEFT ON ITS OWN.

CLEARLY THE PERSON HE WAS DEALING WITH WANTED THE *SARCOPHAGUS* TOO, FORCING HIM TO COME BACK TO GET IT.

DO YOU HAVE ANYTHING YOU'D LIKE TO SAY BEFORE I PLACE YOU UNDER ARREST?

I WANT MY MOMMY!

THE END

WHICH SCOOBY-DOO! CHARACTER ARE YOU?

Take our groovy test and find out!

1. What's your dream job?

a) Chef .... Q
b) Food critic .... Q
c) Research scientist .... Q
d) Mystery writer .... Q
e) Inventor .... Q

2. What are you never without?

a) Your best friend .... Q
b) A snack .... Q
c) Your glasses .... Q
d) Your fashion sense .... Q
e) Your tool kit .... Q

3. Ruh-roh, you're being chased by a monster. What do you do?

a) Run .... Q
b) Hide .... Q
c) Confront them .... Q
d) Get captured .... Q
e) Build a trap .... Q

4. Which word best describes you?

a) Friendly .... Q
b) Sleepy .... Q
c) Clever .... Q
d) Daring .... Q
e) Resourceful .... Q

5. Your favourite colour is...

a) Brown .... Q
b) Green .... Q
c) Orange .... Q
d) Purple .... Q
e) Blue .... Q

6. In your friendship group, you are:

a) The loveable one .... Q
b) The goofy one .... Q
c) The brainy one .... Q
d) The sporty one .... Q
e) The leader .... Q

7. Your bedroom is filled with...

8. a) Toys .... Q.
b) Food wrappers .... Q
c) Books .... Q
d) Clothes .... Q
e) The latest gadgets .... Q

NOW ADD YOUR LETTERS UP!

MOSTLY A

YOU ARE... SCOOBY-DOO

Like Scooby, you're the greatest pal anyone could wish for, even if you can be a bit of a scaredy-cat. Playful but loyal, the only thing bigger than your heart is your appetite!

MOSTLY B

YOU ARE... SHAGGY

Like Shaggy, you're a little on the lazy side. But if a friend's ever in trouble, you're there on the double (providing there are no monsters about). Food makes you happy. *Really* happy!

MOSTLY C

YOU ARE... VELMA

Like Velma, you've got brains to spare. You love figuring out how things work – including people – and like nothing better than curling up with a good book. Life has big plans for you!

MOSTLY D

YOU ARE... DAPHNE

Like Daphne, trouble follows you wherever you go. Although you love looking good, there's more to you than just great clothes. You're naturally sporty and a terrific listener, too!

MOSTLY E

YOU ARE... FRED

Like Fred, you're a natural leader who likes to take charge. You can build or fix anything and are always the first person your friends turn to if there's a problem. You love techy stuff!

HOW TO DRAW SCOOB!

Follow these five steps to sketch your own Scooby-Doo.

FUN FACT
Scooby-Doo has a cousin named Scooby-Dum and a nephew called Scrappy-Doo.

66

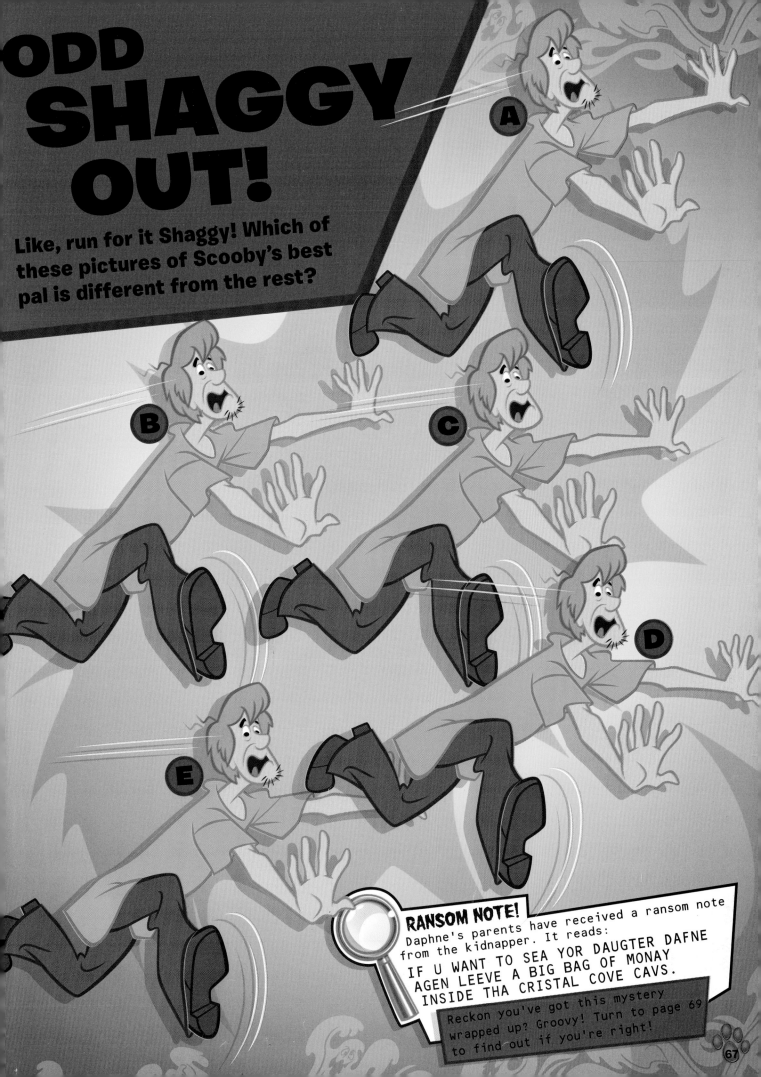

ODD SHAGGY OUT!

Like, run for it Shaggy! Which of these pictures of Scooby's best pal is different from the rest?

RANSOM NOTE!
Daphne's parents have received a ransom note from the kidnapper. It reads:

IF U WANT TO SEA YOR DAUGTER DAFNE AGEN LEEVE A BIG BAG OF MONAY INSIDE THA CRISTAL COVE CAVS.

Reckon you've got this mystery wrapped up? Groovy! Turn to page 69 to find out if you're right!

MUTT MAKE!

SCOOBY-DOO MASK!

LIKE, ASK AN ADULT FOR HELP WHEN YOU'RE USING SCISSORS!

INSTRUCTIONS:

1. Glue this page to a piece of thin card.

2. Wait until the glue is dry then cut out your mask along the dotted lines (taking extra care with the eyeholes).

3. Make two small holes on either side of the mask and thread through string or elastic.

4. Try your Scooby mask on for size!

RELLO!

68

ANSWERS

SNACK POT!

Pages 24-25
SCOOBY-DOO, WHERE ARE YOU?

Pages 10-11
COLLAR COUNT
There are 13 dog tags.

SAME GAME!
They all mean 'dog'.

RUN FOR YOUR RIFE!
Sequence 1:   Sequence 2:   Sequence 3:

Page 26
DUPLICATING DAPHNE!
A & H, D & G, B & F, C & E

Page 34
IT'S TIME TO GUESS THE CRIME
SMUGGLING

LOST AND FOUND

Page 44
...ND I WOULD HAVE GOTTEN AWAY WITH IT TOO,
...IT WEREN'T FOR YOU MEDDLING KIDS!

Pages 36-37
MACHINE MUDDLE
3, 5, 1, 6, 4, 2

FRED RINGER!
B & E are identical.

Pages 46-47
JINKIES, IT'S THE GHOST CLOWN

JEEPERS, IT'S THE CREEPER

ZOINKS, IT'S THE WAX PHANTOM

RUH-ROH, IT'S THE GHOST OF CAPTAIN CUTLER

...OLLY, IT'S THE ...LACK KNIGHT

Page 48
SPOT THE SPOOKY DIFFERENCES

Pages 50-51
SPOOKY SUDOKU

Pages 54-55
EYE TEST!

MISSING OBJECT

MONSTROUS WORD SEARCH!

X	W	I	K	C	H	F	D	N	I	F	GHR
M	L	U	A	M	Z	W	F	D	P	D	RV
G	A	R	G	O	Y	L	E	A	K	S	EB
H	R	F	A	V	I	S	S	Y	D	F	EDM
Q	E	J	G	U	Q	F	S	A	P	K	PN
S	K	E	L	E	T	O	N	Y	L	P	EVI
T	L	Q	U	S	N	F	X	K	A	O	RZ
N	A	Z	C	W	E	R	E	W	O	L	F
A	M	L	H	B	C	X	S	W	H	T	RZH
M	A	H	G	T	N	C	G	B	U	W	KAM
E	K	U	S	C	Z	H	M	O	T	N	AHP
R	S	A	W	A	O	F	C	B	H	I	FUD
A	L	M	V	U	Z	N	O	M	E	D	ULP
G	A	K	L	S	L	M	X	T	N	A	TUM

TRUE OR FALSE: True.

Page 67
ODD SHAGGY OUT: C

SCOOBY-DOO WHODUNNIT CHALLENGE!
Daphne's kidnapper was **THE SEA DEMON**

Our first clue was Daphne's shoe, which had three unidentified fingerprints on it. By comparing these prints with the prints of our four suspects we were able to rule out the Miner Forty-Niner.

Our second clue was the eyewitness account. The mall parking attendant distinctly heard Daphne shout: "Let me go, you green meanie!" This ruled out the Indian Witch Doctor, whose mask and robes are pink, orange, yellow and black in colour - but definitely not green.

Our final clue was the ransom note received by Daphne's parents. Almost every other word was spelt incorrectly. This ruled out the Swamp Zombie, who - as stated in his profile - is 'top monster' when it comes to spelling.

Piecing all these clues together left just one possible culprit: THE SEA DEMON, who is now cooling off behind bars. Great job, gang!